This Book Belongs To:

_____

COPYRIGHT © 2004 Nanci Bell
Gander Publishing
P.O. Box 780, 450 Front Street
Avila Beach, CA 93424
805-541-5523 • 800-554-1819

VISUALIZING AND VERBALIZING AND V/V ARE REGISTERED TRADEMARKS OF NANCI BELL.

15   14   13   12   7   8   9   10

ISBN 0-945856-36-9   978-0-945856-36-8

7-120615

Overview and Directions

This workbook is designed to develop gestalt imagery and language comprehension with the *Visualizing and Verbalizing for Language Comprehension and Thinking*® (V/V®) program.

Following the steps of V/V, detail and gestalt imagery are developed with Sentence by Sentence, Multiple Sentence, Whole Paragraph, and Paragraph by Paragraph V/V stimulation.

Each story is high in imagery and followed by these workbook activities:

- Imagery Questions
- Picture Summary
- Word Summary
- Main Idea
- Higher Order Thinking (HOT) Questions
- Paragraph Writing

As the student begins each story, he/she should decode the vocabulary words and visualize the meaning. This will help create imagery and develop contextual fluency. The student may write phrases or partial sentences to describe his/her imagery.

These workbooks have been written specifically to help students learn and discover the wonder of the written word by improving gestalt imagery, critical thinking, and writing skills. Once these skills are developed, the possibilities are endless.

Remember, you can help students do this. You can do anything!

Nanci Bell
2004

There are three workbooks at each reading level:

Book A • Sentence by Sentence
Book B • Sentence by Sentence and Multiple Sentence
Book C • Multiple Sentence, Whole Paragraph, and Paragraph by Paragraph

Meet Ivan!

I am Ivan, King of the Neighborhood. I'm big and wide and full of pride!

I **love** to eat!

I **love** to sleep!

I am a cat!

1 The Snail

The snail is a soft-bodied animal that is covered with a hard shell. A snail has a muscular foot instead of legs. The snail uses his foot to slide over the ground. He makes a sticky slime to help him glide smoothly over sharp rocks and not get hurt. Snails cannot see very well. So he has two long tentacles on his head to help him move around.

Vocabulary:

soft-bodied: having a body that is very soft
muscular: strong; powerful
slime: a thick liquid
glide: move smoothly and easily
tentacles: long thin finger-like parts that are on a snail's head

---

1 **First and Second Sentences:** The snail is a soft-bodied animal that is covered with a hard shell. A snail has a muscular foot instead of legs.

What did those words make you picture? _____

_____

1. What did you picture for the snail? _____

_____

2. What did you see for the snail's shell? _____

_____

3. What color did you picture his shell? _____

_____

4. What did you see for the snail's one foot? _____

---

2 **Third and Fourth Sentences:** The snail uses his foot to slide over the ground. He makes a sticky slime to help him glide smoothly over sharp rocks and not get hurt.

What did those words make you picture? _____

_____

1. What did you picture for the snail's foot sliding on the ground? _____

_____

2. What did you see for the slime? _____

_____

3. How did you see the snail gliding over the rocks? _____

_____

4. What did you see for the snail not getting hurt? _____

3 — Fifth and Sixth Sentences: Snails cannot see very well. So he has two long tentacles on his head to help him move around.

What did those words make you picture? _____

_____

1. What did you picture for the snail not seeing well? _____

_____

2. What did you see for the tentacles? _____

_____

3. What size did you picture the tentacles? _____

_____

4. What did you see for the snail moving? _____

_____

Picture Summary:

Number your images in order.

[   ] The snail uses his foot to glide over the ground.

[   ] The snail has a muscular foot instead of legs.

[   ] The snail can't see very well, but he has two long tentacles to help him move around.

[   ] The snail makes a sticky slime to help guide him over sharp rocks.

Write a Word Summary:

_____

_____

_____

_____

_____

_____

Critical Thinking

Main Idea:

Check the box that best describes all your images—the main idea.

☐ The snail has a hard shell, one foot, and tentacles to help him move around.

☐ The snail makes a sticky slime to help him glide over sharp rocks.

☐ The snail cannot see very well, but has two long tentacles on his head.

HOT Questions:

1. Why do you think a snail might need a hard shell? _____

_____

2. What might happen to the snail if he only had a soft body and no hard shell? _____

_____

3. Why do you think the snail has just one foot and no legs? _____

_____

4. How does the snail's one foot help him? _____

_____

5. Why do you think the snail makes slime? _____

_____

6. Why do you think the snail needs tentacles? _____

_____

7. How do you think these tentacles help the snail move around? _____

_____

Make up a story about what happened to Sam the Snail one rainy day.

_____
_____
_____
_____
_____
_____
_____
_____
_____
_____
_____
_____
_____
_____
_____
_____

Did you use all of the Structure Words? Check each one you used.

☐ What   ☐ Size   ☐ Color   ☐ Number   ☐ Shape   ☐ Where
☐ Movement   ☐ Mood   ☐ Background   ☐ Perspective   ☐ When   ☐ Sound

2 The Spruce Goose

The Spruce Goose is a huge wooden plane that was only flown one time. The airplane, the largest ever built, has a wingspan of over 300 feet. It could even land on the water. It was built to carry soldiers and equipment in World War II. But by the time the plane was ready, the war was over. Then the Spruce Goose was put in storage. It never flew again.

Vocabulary:

wingspan: the length from the tip of one wing to the tip of the other
storage: a place where something is kept until needed

1 **First and Second Sentences:** The Spruce Goose is a huge wooden plane that was only flown one time. The airplane, the largest ever built, has a wingspan of over 300 feet.

What did those words make you picture? _____

_____

_____

1. What did you see for the Spruce Goose? _____

2. What did you see for it being made of wood rather than metal? _____

3. What did you picture for its wings? _____

4. How did you see "over 300 feet"? Did you picture the number, the large size, or both?

2 **Third and Fourth Sentences:** It could even land on the water. It was built to carry soldiers and equipment in World War II.

What did those words make you picture? _____

_____

_____

1. What did you see for the Spruce Goose landing on water? _____

2. What kind of water did you picture—an ocean, a lake, or...? _____

3. What did you see for it carrying soldiers? _____

4. What did you picture for World War II? _____

5

3 **Fifth, Sixth, and Seventh Sentences:** But by the time the plane was ready, the war was over. Then the Spruce Goose was put in storage. It never flew again.

What did those words make you picture? _____

_____

_____

1. What did you see for the airplane being finished and ready? _____

_____

2. What did you picture for the war being over? _____

_____

3. What did you see for the Spruce Goose being put in storage? _____

_____

4. What did you see happening to the plane if it didn't fly again? _____

_____

Picture Summary:

Number these in order.

[ ] The plane could land on the water, and was built to carry soldiers and equipment.

[ ] By the time the plane was ready, the war was over.

[ ] The plane was put in storage and it never flew again.

[ ] The Spruce Goose is a huge wooden plane with a wingspan of over 300 feet, which has only been flown once.

Write a Word Summary:

_____

_____

_____

_____

_____

_____

_____

Main Idea:

Check the box that best describes all your images—the main idea.

☐ The Spruce Goose is a huge plane that was built to carry soldiers, but was never used.

☐ The Spruce Goose is the largest plane ever built and could even land on water.

☐ The Spruce Goose was built to carry soldiers and equipment in World War II.

HOT Questions:

1. Why do you think the Spruce Goose was made of wood rather than metal? _____

_____

2. How do you think it got its name? _____

_____

3. Why do you think the plane needed such a large wingspan? _____

_____

4. How do you think being made of wood may have helped such a huge airplane to land on water? _____

_____

5. Why might the military have needed a very large airplane? _____

_____

6. Why do you think the plane was only flown once? _____

_____

7. Why do you think the plane was put in storage instead of being destroyed? _____

_____

Make up a story about what the Spruce Goose may have done to help the war if it had been completed in time.

_____

_____

_____

_____

_____

_____

_____

_____

_____

_____

_____

_____

_____

_____

_____

_____

Did you use all of the Structure Words? Check each one you used.

| ☐ What | ☐ Size | ☐ Color | ☐ Number | ☐ Shape | ☐ Where |
| ☐ Movement | ☐ Mood | ☐ Background | ☐ Perspective | ☐ When | ☐ Sound |

3 The First Flight

On December 17, 1903, the Wright brothers made the first airplane flight. They had built a plane with two wings, one above the other. It also had a small engine. The pilot did not have a seat. He had to lie down on the bottom wing and use his hips to move the wings. So, on that windy morning, Orville Wright lay down on the wing and the plane took off. It only flew for 12 seconds, but it was good enough for the first flight.

Vocabulary:

Wright brothers: Wilbur and Orville Wright were two brothers who built the first successful airplane
pilot: the person who flies the airplane

---

1 **First and Second Sentences:** On December 17, 1903, the Wright brothers made the first airplane flight. They had built a plane with two wings, one above the other.

What did those words make you picture? _____

_____

_____

1. What did you see for the Wright brothers?_____

_____

2. How did you picture the date? _____

_____

3. What did you see for the airplane? _____

_____

4. How did you picture one wing above the other? _____

_____

---

2 **Third, Fourth, and Fifth Sentences:** It also had a small engine. The pilot did not have a seat. He had to lie down on the bottom wing and use his hips to move the wings.

What did those words make you picture? _____

_____

_____

1. What did you see for the plane's engine? _____

_____

2. What did you see for the pilot?_____

_____

3. How did you see the pilot on the bottom wing? _____

_____

4. What did you see for the pilot using his hips to move the wings?

_____

3 **Sixth and Seventh Sentences:** So, on that windy morning, Orville Wright lay down on the wing and the plane took off. It only flew for 12 seconds, but it was good enough for the first flight.

What did those words make you picture? _____

_____

_____

1. What did you see for a windy morning? _____

_____

2. What did you see Orville do on the wing? _____

_____

3. What did you see for the plane taking off? _____

_____

4. What mood did you see for the brothers after their airplane made the first flight ever?

_____

Picture Summary:

Number your images in order.

[ ] The Wright brothers made the first successful airplane flight on December 17, 1903.

[ ] Orville Wright lay down on the wing and flew for 12 seconds.

[ ] The plane had a small engine and two wings, one above the other.

[ ] The pilot had no seat and had to use his hips to move the wings.

Write a Word Summary:

_____

_____

_____

_____

_____

_____

_____

Main Idea:

Check the box that best describes all your images—the main idea.

☐ In December 17, 1903, the Wright brothers made the first successful airplane flight.

☐ The pilot had to lie down on the bottom wing and use his hips to move the wings.

☐ The first airplane flight only lasted 12 seconds.

HOT Questions:

1. Why do you think the Wright brothers are such an important part of human history? _____

_____

2. What might be a reason that the pilot did not have a seat? _____

_____

3. Do you think it would be difficult to control the plane while lying down? Why? _____

_____

4. Do you think it would be hard to control the wings by moving your hips? Why? _____

_____

5. Do you think the wind might help or hurt the flight? Why? _____

_____

6. Why do you think this flight only lasted 12 seconds? _____

_____

7. How would the world be different if we didn't have airplanes? _____

_____

Make up an exciting story about the Wright brothers' first flight.

_____

_____

_____

_____

_____

_____

_____

_____

_____

_____

_____

_____

_____

_____

_____

_____

Did you use all of the Structure Words? Check each one you used.

☐ What   ☐ Size   ☐ Color   ☐ Number   ☐ Shape   ☐ Where
☐ Movement ☐ Mood   ☐ Background ☐ Perspective ☐ When   ☐ Sound

4 Paul Bunyan

In the 1800's, lumberjacks would sit around their campfires at night and tell tales of Paul Bunyan. The stories said Paul was a huge man and a great lumberjack. He could chop down two trees with one swing of his ax. He was so big that he needed a lot of food. He would eat so many pancakes that the cooks had to make a special grill. The grill was so big, the cooks tied slabs of bacon on their feet. Then they skated across the grill to grease it.

Vocabulary:

lumberjack: a person whose job is to cut down trees
grill: a flat metal plate that food is cooked on
slabs: big thick pieces before they are sliced

---

1 **First and Second Sentences:** In the 1800's, lumberjacks would sit around their campfires at night and tell tales of Paul Bunyan. The stories said Paul was a huge man and a great lumberjack.

What did those words make you picture? _____

_____

_____

1. What did you see for a lumberjack? _____

2. What did you see for the lumberjacks sitting around their campfire? _____

3. What did you see for them telling stories? _____

4. What did you see for Paul Bunyan? _____

---

2 **Third, Fourth, and Fifth Sentences:** He could chop down two trees with one swing of his ax. He was so big that he needed a lot of food. He would eat so many pancakes that the cooks had to make a special grill.

What did those words make you picture? _____

_____

_____

1. What did you see for Paul Bunyan chopping down trees? _____

2. What did you see for the size of Paul's ax? _____

3. What did you see for Paul eating pancakes? _____

4. How did you picture the special grill? _____

3 **Sixth and Seventh Sentences:** The grill was so big, the cooks tied slabs of bacon on their feet. Then they skated across the grill to grease it.

What did those words make you picture? _____

_____

_____

1. What did you see for the cooks? _____

_____

2. What did you see for the bacon on their feet? _____

_____

3. How did you picture the bacon tied on their feet? _____

_____

4. What did you see for the cooks skating on the grill? _____

_____

Picture Summary:

Number your images in order.

☐ The cooks tied slabs of bacon to their feet and skated across the grill to grease it.

☐ Paul Bunyan was so huge, he could chop down two trees with one swing of his ax.

☐ In the 1800's, lumberjacks would sit around their campfires and tell tales of Paul Bunyan.

☐ Paul Bunyan would eat so many pancakes that the cooks had to make a special grill.

Write a Word Summary:

_____

_____

_____

_____

_____

_____

_____

Critical Thinking

Main Idea:

Check the box that best describes all your images—the main idea.

☐ Paul Bunyan was a huge man who could chop down two trees with one swing of his ax.

☐ Paul Bunyan could eat so many pancakes that the cooks needed a huge grill to cook them.

☐ Lumberjacks told tales of a huge man name Paul Bunyan who was very strong and ate a lo

HOT Questions:

1. Why do you think the lumberjacks told stories of Paul Bunyan? _____

_____

2. Why do you think they told these stories around their campfires at night?_____

_____

3. Why do you think the stories said that Paul was a great lumberjack and not a cowboy or something else? _____

_____

4. Why do you think the stories said Paul was a big man and not a small one?_____

_____

5. Why do you think the cooks in the story needed such a big grill? _____

_____

6. Do you think tying slabs of bacon to their feet and skating across the grill was a good way to grease it? Why?___

_____

7. What other stories do you think lumberjacks might have made up about Paul Bunyan? _____

_____

15

Make up a wild tale about something Paul Bunyan might do!

_____

_____

_____

_____

_____

_____

_____

_____

_____

_____

_____

_____

_____

_____

_____

_____

_____

Did you use all of the Structure Words? Check each one you used.

| ☐ What | ☐ Size | ☐ Color | ☐ Number | ☐ Shape | ☐ Where |
| ☐ Movement | ☐ Mood | ☐ Background | ☐ Perspective | ☐ When | ☐ Sound |

5 The Deepest Mine

The shaft of the Western Deep gold mine in South Africa sinks three miles deep into the Earth. It is the deepest mine in the world. The mine is so deep that it takes hours for workers to go to the bottom. The temperature in the mine can reach 150 degrees. Huge air conditioners keep the air close to a hot 100 degrees. Even the rock walls are hot to touch. But for hours, the workers dig out the rich ore and send it to the surface. Then the pure gold will be taken out of the ore and sold around the world.

Vocabulary:

mine: a deep hole in the Earth from where gold, coal, or other minerals are removed
shaft: a long straight hole
South Africa: a country on the bottom tip of Africa
ore: rock or dirt that has lots of gold or other metals in it

---

1 **First and Second Sentences:** The shaft of the Western Deep gold mine in South Africa sinks three miles deep into the Earth. It is the deepest mine in the world.

What did those words make you picture? _____

_____

_____

1. What did you see for the gold mine? _____

_____

2. What did you picture for South Africa? _____

_____

3. What did you see for the mine shaft? _____

_____

4. How did you see it being three miles deep? _____

_____

---

2 **Third and Fourth Sentences:** The mine is so deep that it takes hours for workers to go to the bottom. The temperature in the mine can reach 150 degrees.

What did those words make you picture? _____

_____

_____

1. What did you see for the workers? _____

_____

2. What did you see for them going to the bottom of the mine? _____

_____

3. What did you picture for the temperature? _____

_____

4. What did you feel in your imagery for 150 degrees of heat? _____

_____

3 **Fifth and Sixth Sentences:** Huge air conditioners keep the air close to a hot 100 degrees. Even the rock walls are hot to touch.

What did those words make you picture? _____

_____

_____

1. What did you see for the air conditioners? _____

2. How could you see them "huge"? _____

3. What did you picture for the rock walls in the mine?_____

4. What did you see for the walls being hot to touch? _____

_____

4 **Seventh and Eighth Sentences:** But for hours, the workers dig out the rich ore and send it to the surface. Then the pure gold will be taken out of the ore and sold around the world.

What did those words make you picture? _____

_____

_____

1. What did you see for the workers digging?_____

2. What did you picture for the ore? _____

3. What color did you see for the gold that came out of the ore? _____

4. What did you picture for the gold being sold around the world?_____

_____

Picture Summary:

Number your images in order.

The workers dig out the rich ore and send it to the surface to have the pure gold removed from it.

Huge air conditioners keep the air at around 100 degrees.

The shaft of the Western Deep gold mine in South Africa sinks more than three miles deep into the Earth.

It can take hours for the workers to go to the bottom, where the temperature can reach 150 degrees.

Write a Word Summary:

_____

_____

_____

_____

_____

_____

Critical Thinking

Main Idea:

Check the box that best describes all your images—the main idea.

☐ The mine in South Africa sinks three miles deep into the Earth.

☐ Workers dig for gold in very hot temperatures in the Western Deep mine, the world's deepest mine.

☐ The temperature in the Western Deep mine can reach 150 degrees.

HOT Questions:

1. Why do you think the mining company would build a mine so deep in the Earth? _____

_____

2. Why do you think it takes so long to reach the bottom? _____

_____

3. How do you think the workers get to the bottom of the mine? _____

_____

4. Why do you think the mine has air conditioners at the bottom? _____

_____

5. How might the hot temperature make working in the mine difficult? _____

_____

6. Why might the rock walls being hot make it difficult for the miners? _____

_____

7. Would you like to work in a gold mine? Why or why not? _____

_____

Make up a scary story about working in the Western Deep gold mine.

_____

_____

_____

_____

_____

_____

_____

_____

_____

_____

_____

_____

_____

_____

_____

_____

_____

_____

_____

_____

Did you use all of the Structure Words? Check each one you used.

| ☐ What | ☐ Size | ☐ Color | ☐ Number | ☐ Shape | ☐ Where |
| ☐ Movement | ☐ Mood | ☐ Background | ☐ Perspective | ☐ When | ☐ Sound |

6 The Frisbee

The Frisbee got its name from the Frisbie Pie Company. The pies were popular with students in the 1800's. The pies were sold in thin pie tins. After the pie was eaten, the students would throw the tins back and forth. Then in 1948, Fred Morrison made a plastic Frisbee. The plastic toys flew better than the old pie tins. Since then, the Frisbee has been one of the most loved toys in the world.

Vocabulary:

frisbee: a plastic toy that is shaped like a disk and is thrown back and forth
pie tin: a small metal pie plate

---

1 **First and Second Sentences:** The Frisbee got its name from the Frisbie Pie Company. The pies were popular with students in the 1800's.

What did those words make you picture? _____

_____

_____

1. What did you picture for a Frisbee? _____

2. What color was your Frisbee? _____

3. What did you see for a pie company? _____

4. What did you see for the pies being popular with students? _____

---

2 **Third and Fourth Sentences:** The pies were sold in thin pie tins. After the pie was eaten, the students would throw the tins back and forth.

What did those words make you picture? _____

_____

_____

1. What did you picture for the pie tins? _____

2. What did you see for the pie tin after the pie was eaten? _____

3. How did you see the students throwing the pie tins? _____

4. What color did you see for the tins? _____

3

Fifth, Sixth, and Seventh Sentences: Then in 1948, Fred Morrison made a plastic Frisbee. The plastic toys flew better than the old pie tins. Since then, the Frisbee has been one of the most loved toys in the world.

What did those words make you picture? _____

_____

_____

1. What did you see for the plastic Frisbee? _____

_____

2. How did you picture the plastic Frisbee flying better than the old pie tins?

_____

3. What did you see for the Frisbee being a loved toy? _____

_____

4. What could you hear in your imagery? _____

_____

Picture Summary:

Number your images in order.

☐ Students would throw the tins back and forth after the pie was gone.

☐ The Frisbee got its name from the Frisbie Pie Company in the 1800s.

☐ In 1948, Fred Morrison made a plastic Frisbee and it flew better than the old pie tins.

☐ Since then, the Frisbee has been one of the most loved toys in the world.

Write a Word Summary:

_____

_____

_____

_____

_____

_____

Critical Thinking

Main Idea:

Check the box that best describes all your images—the main idea.

☐ The Frisbie Pie Company made pies that were popular with students in the 1800's.

☐ In 1948, Fred Morrison made a plastic Frisbee.

☐ The Frisbee is a popular toy that began when students threw empty pie tins to each other

HOT Questions:

1. Why do you think the Frisbee was named after the pie company? _____

_____

2. Why do you think students liked the pies? _____

_____

3. Do you think it was important that students were playing with their empty pie tins? Explain. _____

_____

4. Why do you think the students decided to throw the tins back and forth? _____

_____

5. What might have happened if students hadn't started throwing pie tins? _____

_____

6. What might be a reason why the plastic Frisbees flew better than the pie tins? _____

_____

7. Why might plastic Frisbees be better than tin Frisbees? _____

_____

Make up a story about something funny or scary happening when throwing a Frisbee.

_____

_____

_____

_____

_____

_____

_____

_____

_____

_____

_____

_____

_____

_____

_____

_____

Did you use all of the Structure Words? Check each one you used.

☐ What	☐ Size	☐ Color	☐ Number	☐ Shape	☐ Where
☐ Movement	☐ Mood	☐ Background	☐ Perspective	☐ When	☐ Sound

7 The Eiffel Tower

The Eiffel Tower stands 986 feet high in Paris. The huge iron structure was built for the 1889 World's Fair. It took two years for the 300 steel workers to build it. Then 40 tons of brown paint was applied. Two million people came to see the tower in its first year. Since then, 200 million more have come. Most people ride the elevators to the top. Then they look at the best view in all of Paris.

Vocabulary:

Eiffel Tower: a large iron tower that stands in Paris, France
Paris: the city that is the capital of France
structure: a building
applied: spread on; put on

---

1 **First and Second Sentences:** The Eiffel Tower stands 986 feet high in Paris. The huge iron structure was built for the 1889 World's Fair.

What did those words make you picture? _____
_____

1. What did you see for the Eiffel Tower? _____
_____

2. What did you see for Paris? _____
_____

3. How did you see 986 feet high? _____
_____

4. What did you picture for the 1889 World's Fair? _____
_____

---

2 **Third and Fourth Sentences:** It took two years for the 300 steel workers to build it. Then 40 tons of brown paint was applied.

What did those words make you picture? _____
_____

1. What did you see for the steel workers? _____
_____

2. How did you see the workers building the tower? _____
_____

3. What did you picture for the paint? _____
_____

4. What kind of containers did you see the paint in—small, large, very large, or...?
_____

25

3 **Fifth and Sixth Sentences:** Two million people came to see the tower in its first year. Since then, 200 million more have come.

What did those words make you picture? _____

_____

_____

1. What did you see for the people who came to the World's Fair in 1889?

   _____

2. What did you see for how the people were dressed? _____

   _____

3. What did you see for the people that now come to visit? _____

   _____

4. How many people did you see having visited the tower since 1889?

4 **Seventh and Eighth Sentences:** Most people ride the elevators to the top. Then they look at the best view in all of Paris.

What did those words make you picture? _____

_____

_____

1. What did you see for the elevators? _____

   _____

2. How did you see the elevators going to the top? _____

   _____

3. What did you see for people getting to the very top? _____

   _____

4. What did you see the people looking at from way up high? _____

Picture Summary:

Number your images in order.

The Eiffel Tower had over two million visitors in its first year, and more than 200 million since then.

The Eiffel Tower stands 986 feet high and was built for the 1889 World's Fair in Paris.

Most people ride the elevators to the top to see the best view in Paris.

It took two years for 300 steel workers to build the Eiffel Tower.

Write a Word Summary:

_____

_____

_____

_____

_____

Main Idea:

Check the box that best describes all your images—the main idea.

☐ Since it was opened in 1889, the Eiffel Tower has been a popular tourist attraction.

☐ The Eiffel Tower is a huge iron structure that was built for the 1889 World's Fair and has since become a tourist attraction in Paris.

☐ The Eiffel Tower is 986 feet high and took over two years to build.

HOT Questions:

1. Why do you think the Eiffel Tower took so long to build? _____

_____

2. Why do you think 300 steel workers were needed to build the tower? _____

_____

3. Why did the tower need so much paint the first year and do you think it still needs to be painted? _____

_____

4. Why do you think so many people came to visit the tower during its first year? _____

_____

5. Do you think that people come now for the same reasons as the first visitors? Why? _____

_____

6. Why do you think visitors go to the top of the Eiffel Tower? _____

_____

7. Why do you think some people take the elevators instead of climbing to the top? _____

_____

Make up a story about climbing to the top of the Eiffel Tower in a storm.

_____
_____
_____
_____
_____
_____
_____
_____
_____
_____
_____
_____
_____
_____
_____
_____
_____
_____
_____

Did you use all of the Structure Words? Check each one you used.

☐ What	☐ Size	☐ Color	☐ Number	☐ Shape	☐ Where
☐ Movement	☐ Mood	☐ Background	☐ Perspective	☐ When	☐ Sound

8 The Yo-Yo

About 500 years ago, people in the Philippines used yo-yos to hunt. They would throw stone yo-yos at an animal. The string would wrap around the animal's legs and make it fall. Later, small wood yo-yos were used as toys. A young man brought these toys with him when he moved to the U.S. People would stare as the man played with his toys on his breaks from work. Soon, he started a company and his yo-yos became popular with children and adults.

Vocabulary:

yo-yo: a toy that is made of two round pieces of wood or plastic that are joined and have a long piece of string in the middle
Philippines: a country in the Pacific Ocean that is made up of thousands of islands

---

1 **First, Second, and Third Sentences:** About 500 years ago, people in the Philippines used yo-yos to hunt. They would throw stone yo-yos at an animal. The string would wrap around the animal's legs and make it fall.

What did those words make you picture? _____

_____

_____

1. What did you see for a stone yo-yo? _____

_____

2. What did you see for people throwing it at an animal? _____

_____

3. What did you see the string doing? _____

_____

4. What did you see for the animal falling down? _____

_____

---

2 **Fourth and Fifth Sentences:** Later, small wood yo-yos were used as toys. A young man brought these toys with him when he moved to the U.S.

What did those words make you picture? _____

_____

_____

1. What did you see for a wooden yo-yo? _____

_____

2. What color did you picture the yo-yo? _____

_____

3. What did you see for the young man? _____

_____

4. What did you see for him coming to the U.S.? _____

_____

3 **Sixth and Seventh Sentences:** People would stare as the man played with his toys on his breaks from work. Soon, he started a company and his yo-yos became popular with children and adults.

What did those words make you picture? _____

_____

1. What did you see for people staring at the man? _____

_____

2. What did you see the man doing on his breaks at work? _____

_____

3. What did you see for the man's company? _____

_____

4. What did you see for the yo-yo becoming "popular"? _____

_____

Picture Summary:

Number your images in order.

[ ] The yo-yo was first used to hunt in the Philippines about 500 years ago.

[ ] A young man brought wooden yo-yos with him when he moved to the U.S.

[ ] The hunters threw the stone yo-yos at animals and the string would wrap around the animal's legs and make it fall.

[ ] The young man started a company after people stared at him playing with his yo-yo, and his yo-yos became popular.

Write a Word Summary:

_____

_____

_____

_____

_____

_____

_____

Main Idea:

Check the box that best describes all your images—the main idea.

☐ Yo-yos started as weapons, but they became popular as toys in the U.S.

☐ People would stare as the young man played with his yo-yos during his breaks from work.

☐ Stone yo-yos were thrown at an animal and its string would make the animal fall.

HOT Questions:

1. Why do you think that the yo-yos used for hunting were made of stone and not wood? _____

_____

2. Why were stone yo-yos a good way to hunt animals? _____

_____

3. Why were the toys made of wood and not stone? _____

_____

4. What would be bad about having a toy yo-yo made of stone? _____

_____

5. Why do you think the young man brought some yo-yos with him when he moved to the U.S.? _____

_____

6. Why do you think people would stare as the man played with his yo-yos? _____

_____

7. Why do you think yo-yos became so popular with both children and adults? _____

_____

Make up a story about anything you want!

_____

_____

_____

_____

_____

_____

_____

_____

_____

_____

_____

_____

_____

_____

_____

_____

Did you use all of the Structure Words? Check each one you used.

☐ What   ☐ Size   ☐ Color   ☐ Number   ☐ Shape   ☐ Where
☐ Movement   ☐ Mood   ☐ Background   ☐ Perspective   ☐ When   ☐ Sound

The Owl Butterfly

Owl butterflies are often mistaken for birds or bats. They are one of the world's biggest butterflies. They have yellow and brown spots on each wing that look just like the eyes of an owl. They drink sap from trees. Since they come out at dusk, birds think they are deadly owls in the trees and leave them alone.

Vocabulary:

butterflies: a type of beautiful insect with colorful wings
sap: the liquid that is in plants and trees
dusk: when the sun begins to go down

1

What did those words make you picture? _____

_____

_____

1. What did you picture for the owl butterfly? _____

_____

2. What did you picture for the size of an owl butterfly? _____

_____

3. What colors did you picture for the eyes of an owl? _____

_____

4. Where did you picture the owl butterfly drinking? _____

_____

5. What did you picture birds doing when they see an owl butterfly? _____

_____

Critical Thinking

Write a Word Summary:

_____

_____

_____

_____

Main Idea:

Check the box that best describes all your images—the main idea.

☐ Owl butterflies have spots on their wings that look like an owl's eyes and birds leave them alone.

☐ Owl butterflies are often mistaken for birds or bats.

☐ Owl butterflies have yellow and brown spots on each wing that look just like an owl's eyes.

HOT Questions:

1. Why do you think owl butterflies are mistaken for birds or bats?_____

_____

2. Why do you think owl butterflies have yellow and brown spots on their wings?_____

_____

3. Why do you think the owl butterfly might look like an owl?_____

_____

4. Why do you think looking like an owl might help the butterfly?_____

_____

5. Why do you think the butterflies may only come out at dusk?_____

_____

6. Why do you think the birds leave the "owl" alone?_____

10 Roman Bathtime

In ancient Rome, everyone went to the public pools to take a bath. Called bathhouses, these were grand places with huge pools and fine art. Women went to one bathhouse and men to their own. After a bath in a hot pool, a person might go take a dip in a cool pool. They might work out with weights and balls. While bathing, Romans chatted with their friends, so a bath could take hours.

Vocabulary:

ancient Rome: during the Roman Empire, from 27 B.C. to A.D. 476
bathhouse: a public place where people take baths, relax, and talk with friends
grand: large and wonderful
fine art: beautiful paintings, statues, and other works

1

What did those words make you picture? _____

_____

_____

1. What did you picture for a Roman bathhouse? _____

_____

2. What did you picture for how the people bathed? _____

_____

3. What did you picture for women in one and men in another? _____

_____

4. What did you picture for the people working out? _____

_____

5. How did you picture the people visiting with each other and taking a long time in the bath? _____

_____

Critical Thinking

Write a Word Summary:

_____

_____

_____

_____

Main Idea:

Check the box that best describes all your images—the main idea.

☐ The Roman bathhouses were beautiful places where people went to wash, relax, and visit with each other.

☐ The Roman bathhouses were grand places with huge pools.

☐ While bathing, Romans chatted with their friends, so that a bath could take hours.

IOT Questions:

1. Why do you think people went to a public pool and not to their own bathrooms?_____

_____

2. Why do you think the bathhouses had huge pools?_____

_____

3. Why do you think bathhouses had fine art?_____

_____

4. Why do you think women and men went to separate bathhouses?_____

_____

5. Why do you think there were both hot and cool pools? _____

_____

6. Why do you think there were weights and balls at the bathhouses?_____

11 The Capybara

The capybara, found in South America, looks like a huge hamster. He is brown and furry and the size of a big fat dog. He is the world's biggest rodent. He has small ears on the top of his head and his toes are webbed. He is a good swimmer and loves to roll in the mud. If he is on the bank and hears a scary sound, he dives into the water and hides. He can stay underwater for a few minutes at a time.

Vocabulary:

South America: a large continent that is south of North America
hamster: a small furry animal that many people keep as pets
rodent: a small furry animal that is related to rats and mice
webbed: to have skin between the toes

1

What did those words make you picture? _____

_____

_____

1. What did you picture for a capybara? _____

_____

2. What color and size did you picture the capybara? _____

_____

3. What did you picture for the capybara's ears and toes? _____

_____

4. What did you picture capybara's doing when he hears a scary sound? _____

_____

5. Where did you picture the capybara living? _____

Critical Thinking

Write a Word Summary:

_____

_____

_____

_____

Main Idea:

Check the box that best describes all your images—the main idea.

☐ The capybara, the world's largest rodent, lives near rivers in South America.

☐ The capybara dives into the water and hides when he hears a scary sound.

☐ The capybara has small ears on the top of his head and webbed toes.

HOT Questions:

1. Why is it unusual to have a rodent the size of a dog?_____

_____

2. Why do you think the capybara's toes are webbed? _____

_____

3. Why do you think the capybara is a good swimmer?_____

_____

4. Why do you think the capybara rolls in the mud? _____

_____

5. Why do you think the capybara dives into the water and hides? _____

_____

6. Why do you think the capybara stays under the water for a few minutes?_____

_____

12 The Armored Pangolin

The pangolin, an anteater, is from Africa and has its own armor on its short body. The armor is made of thick pointy brown scales that protect him from danger. When scared, he rolls up into a ball to make himself hard and he looks like a pinecone. He does not look good to eat. He also gives off a bad smell that chases the enemy away.

Vocabulary:

pangolin: a small animal that lives in Asia and Africa and is covered with hard scales
Africa: a continent that is south of Europe
armor: a hard outer covering that protects an animal from harm
scales: hard plates that cover the body

1

What did those words make you picture? _____

_____

_____

1. What did you picture for the pangolin? _____

_____

2. What did you picture for the pangolin's own armor? _____

_____

3. What did you picture for pangolin's pointy scales? _____

_____

4. What did you picture the scales doing when the pangolin rolls into a ball? _____

_____

5. What did you picture for the smell? _____

_____

Critical Thinking

Write a Word Summary:

_____

_____

_____

_____

HOT Questions:

1. Why do you think the pangolin has armor? _____

_____

2. Why do you think the pangolin's scales are thick and pointy? _____

_____

3. How do you think the scales might protect him from danger? _____

_____

4. Why do you think the pangolin rolls into a ball? _____

_____

5. Why do you think the pangolin looks like a pinecone? _____

_____

6. Why do you think the pangolin gives off a bad smell? _____

_____

Main Idea:

Check the box that best describes all your images—the main idea.

☐ The pangolin is well protected with its covering of thick scales and its bad smell.

☐ When scared, the pangolin rolls up into a ball and looks like a pinecone.

☐ The pangolin has an armor made of thick pointy brown scales.

13 Orca

Each killer whale, or orca, has a pattern on his back of black and white that is his alone. No other whale has the same markings. Orcas live in the world's oceans and hunt for fish, squid, seals, and dolphins. A group, or pod, of orcas hunts as a team and shares the food. They seem to know each other and talk through high-pitched whines and moans. Each whale is unique, but they all work together to hunt and raise their calves.

Vocabulary:

pattern: a set of colors or markings
markings: a set of colors and shapes on an animal
squid: a long sea animal with ten arms
pod: a group or family of whales
high-pitched: with a very high sound

1 What did those words make you picture? _____

_____

1. What did you picture for the killer whale? _____

_____

2. What colors did you picture for the whale's pattern? _____

_____

3. What did you picture for killer whale food? _____

_____

4. What did you picture for a pod of orcas? _____

_____

5. What did you hear for the sounds the whales make? _____

Critical Thinking

Write a Word Summary:

_____

_____

_____

_____

Main Idea:

Check the box that best describes all your images—the main idea.

☐ Killer whales live and hunt together as they travel the seas.

☐ A group of killer whales hunts as a team.

☐ A group of killer whales talk to each other through high-pitched whines and moans.

HOT Questions:

1. Why do you think killer whales have individual markings? _____

_____

2. Why do you think killer whales can be easily recognized? _____

_____

3. Why do you think the whales hunt in a group or pod? _____

_____

4. What do you think would be the advantage of hunting in a group? _____

_____

5. Why do you think the whales share their food? _____

_____

6. Why do you think the whales talk to each other? _____

14 The Long Jumper

A jerboa is a tiny mouse that can jump as far as ten feet at a time. He has long silky brown fur and big round eyes that can see in the dark. He has back legs nearly as long as his body. These strong legs lift the tiny mouse far into the air to get away from enemies. He also uses his long tail to help him jump out of danger.

Vocabulary:

jerboa: a mouse that looks like a small kangaroo

silky: very soft and shiny

1

What did those words make you picture? _____

_____

_____

1. What did you picture for the jerboa?_____

_____

2. What did you picture for the jerboa's eyes seeing in the dark?_____

_____

3. What did you picture for the jerboa's back legs? _____

_____

4. What did you picture for the jerboa jumping into the air to get away from his enemies? _____

_____

5. What did you picture for the jerboa's tail?_____

Critical Thinking

Write a Word Summary:

_____

_____

_____

_____

Main Idea:

Check the box that best describes all your images—the main idea.

☐ The jerboa is a small mouse with long legs that help him jump away from enemies.

☐ The jerboa has long silky brown fur.

☐ The jerboa is a tiny mouse with long back legs.

HOT Questions:

1. Why do you think the tiny jerboa mouse can jump as far as ten feet? _____

_____

2. Why do you think the jerboa has big eyes? _____

_____

3. Do you think the jerboa might come out in day or at night? Explain. _____

_____

4. Why do you think the jerboa's legs are nearly as long as his body? _____

_____

5. Why do you think the jerboa uses his tail to help him jump? _____

_____

6. Why do you think the jerboa might need to jump far? _____

_____

15 John Muir

John Muir, a thin man with a long beard, wandered the wild forests, learning about them. He wrote about the redwood trees and wildlife. He drew pictures of the things he saw. He spoke out about how to protect these places. He never gave up and soon people began to listen. Because of Muir, huge areas of land became parks where people could visit and see nature left alone.

Vocabulary:

wandered: to walk from place to place with no reason or destination
redwood trees: the tallest trees in the world
wildlife: wild birds and animals in nature
protect: to keep safe

1

What did those words make you picture? _____

_____

_____

1. What did you picture for John Muir? _____

_____

2. What did you picture for John's beard? _____

_____

3. What did you see for where John wandered? _____

_____

4. What did you picture for what John did to protect wildlife? _____

_____

5. What did you see for a park? _____

_____

Critical Thinking

Write a Word Summary:

_____

_____

_____

_____

Main Idea:

Check the box that best describes all your images—the main idea.

☐ John Muir was a thin man with a long beard who wrote about redwood trees.

☐ John Muir loved nature and convinced people to create parks to protect wildlife.

☐ John Muir spoke to people about nature.

HOT Questions:

1. Why do you think John Muir wandered the wild forests? _____

_____

2. Why do you think John had a long beard instead of shaving every day? _____

_____

3. Why do you think John wrote about and drew pictures of the things he saw? _____

_____

4. Why do you think John began to speak out? _____

_____

5. What do you think John wanted to protect the wild forests from? _____

_____

6. What do you think might have happened to the wild forests if John hadn't been born? _____

_____

16 Man of War

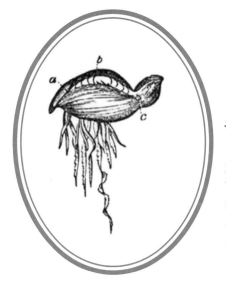

The Portuguese Man-of-War is a jellyfish-like creature that lives in the ocean. It uses a blue gas-filled bag to float in the water. Down from the float trail white and blue strings that have stingers all over them. A fish may swim into this net of stingers, and then is drawn up to the Man-of-War's mouth. The strings also protect the delicate creature from anyone who wants to eat it.

Vocabulary:

gas-filled bag: a balloon-like bag that is filled with gas to help the Man-of-War float
stingers: string-like arms that give off a poison
drawn up: is moved or taken up
delicate: easy to harm or injure

1 What did those words make you picture? _____

_____

1. What did you picture for the gas-filled bag? _____

2. What color did you picture the strings? _____

3. What did you see for stingers? _____

4. What did you see for the fish swimming into the net of stingers? _____

5. What did you see for the Man-of-War eating the fish? _____

Critical Thinking

Write a Word Summary:

_____

_____

_____

_____

Main Idea:

Check the box that best describes all your images—the main idea.

☐ The Portuguese Man-of-War is a strange creature that uses its stingers for protection and to get food.

☐ The Portuguese Man-of-War has a trail of white and blue strings.

☐ The Portuguese Man-of-War uses a blue gas-filled bag to float in the water.

IOT Questions:

1. Why do you think the Man-of-War has a gas-filled bag? _____

_____

2. Why do you think the bag floats on the water? _____

_____

3. Why do you think the Man-of-War has strings that hang down? _____

_____

4. Why do you think the stingers are all over the strings and not just at the ends? _____

_____

5. Why do you think a fish might swim into the strings? _____

_____

6. Why do you think the Man-of-War is considered delicate? _____

_____

17 Gold Rush!

The California Gold Rush began when James Marshall found gold in a river. He was building a new sawmill. When he stepped back to look at his work, he saw a sparkling yellow rock in the river. He reached down and picked up the stone. Gold!

Word soon spread of Marshall's find. People began to dream of all the wealth they could have from mining gold. Soon people from all over the world were on their way to California. The Gold Rush had begun.

Vocabulary:

California: a state in the western part of the U.S.

Gold Rush: the time after gold was discovered in 1848 when thousands of people went to California

sawmill: a place where logs are cut into boards

wealth: money; riches

mining: digging in the Earth to find gold, silver, or other minerals

---

1 **First Paragraph:** The California Gold Rush began when James Marshall found gold in a river. He was building a new sawmill. When he stepped back to look at his work, he saw a sparkling yellow rock in the river. He reached down and picked up the stone. Gold!

What did those words make you picture? _____

_____

1. What did you picture for the words the "California Gold Rush"? _____

_____

2. What did you see for Marshall building a sawmill? _____

_____

3. What did you picture for the rock Marshall saw in the river? _____

_____

4. What did you see for Marshall picking up the stone? _____

_____

2 **Second Paragraph:** Word soon spread of Marshall's find. People began to dream of all the wealth they could have from mining gold. Soon people from all over the world were on their way to California. The Gold Rush had begun.

What did those words make you picture? _____

_____

_____

1. What did you picture for the word spreading about Marshall's find?_____

_____

2. What did you see for people dreaming about gold? _____

_____

3. What did you picture for people coming to California from all over the world? _____

_____

4. What did you picture for how they traveled to California? _____

_____

Picture Summary:

Number these in order.

People rushed to California from all over the world.

The word spread quickly after Marshall found gold.

Marshall saw a sparkling yellow rock in the river.

Marshall was building a new sawmill on the river.

Write a Word Summary:

_____

_____

_____

_____

_____

Critical Thinking

Main Idea:

Check the box that best describes all your images—the main idea.

☐ After James Marshall found gold in a river, people went to California in search of riches, and the California Gold Rush began.

☐ James Marshall saw a sparkling yellow rock in the river and a lot of people came to find one like it.

☐ People from all over the world were on their way to California to find gold.

HOT Questions:

1. Why do you think the story said that Marshall began the California Gold Rush? _____

_____

2. How did building a sawmill start the Gold Rush? _____

_____

3. Why do you think Marshall looked into the river? _____

_____

4. Why do you think Marshall picked up the yellow rock?_____

_____

5. Why do you think people dreamed of mining the gold?_____

_____

6. Why do you think people came to California from all over the world? _____

_____

7. Why do you think this time was called the Gold *Rush*? _____

_____

Make up an exciting story about finding gold.

_____

_____

_____

_____

_____

_____

_____

_____

_____

_____

_____

_____

_____

_____

_____

_____

_____

_____

Did you use all of the Structure Words? Check each one you used.

☐ What   ☐ Size   ☐ Color   ☐ Number   ☐ Shape   ☐ Where
☐ Movement   ☐ Mood   ☐ Background   ☐ Perspective   ☐ When   ☐ Sound

18 Pompeii is Lost

One morning in A.D. 79, the earth shook in the town of Pompeii. Cattle and horses paced nervously in the fields. But it did not seem serious. Most people went about their daily lives. They did not know their lives were about to change. They did not know they were in danger.

With a loud roar, flames and smoke shot out of the volcano, Mt. Vesuvius. Ash and burning stones rained down upon the people of the town. Crowds of people ran through the streets trying to escape. Others hid in their homes. But the ash and poison gases soon found them. Within days, Pompeii disappeared under 30 feet of ash and mud.

For hundreds of years, the city lay hidden. Most people forgot it had been there. Then a man digging in a vineyard found a buried wall. Since then, much of the city has been uncovered. The dead were found in the streets and in their homes. They show a moment that was frozen in time.

Vocabulary:

Pompeii: an ancient town in Italy that was destroyed when a volcano erupted
paced: walked back and forth
Mt. Vesuvius: a volcano in Italy
ash: the powder that is left after something is burned
vineyard: a place where grapes are grown

---

1 **First Paragraph:** One morning in A.D. 79, the earth shook in the town of Pompeii. Cattle and horses paced nervously in the fields. But it did not seem serious. Most people went about their daily lives. They did not know their lives were about to change. They did not know they were in danger.

What did those words make you picture? _____

_____

_____

1. What did you picture for the earth shaking? _____

_____

2. What did you picture for the date? Did you see numbers and letters? Write them. _____

_____

3. What did you picture for the animals pacing in the fields? _____

_____

4. What did you picture for people "going about their daily lives"? _____

_____

2 **Second Paragraph:** With a loud roar, flames and smoke shot out of the volcano, Mt. Vesuvius. Ash and burning stones rained down upon the people of the town. Crowds of people ran through the streets trying to escape. Others hid in their homes. But the ash and poison gases soon found them. Within days, Pompeii disappeared under 30 feet of ash and mud.

What did those words make you picture? _____

_____

1. What did you picture for the volcano? _____

_____

2. What sounds did you hear? _____

_____

3. What did you picture for the ash and stones coming down on the people? _____

_____

4. What did you picture the people doing? _____

_____

3 **Third Paragraph:** For hundreds of years, the city lay hidden. Most people forgot it had been there. Then a man digging in a vineyard found a buried wall. Since then, much of the city has been uncovered. The dead were found in the streets and in their homes. They show a moment that was frozen in time.

What did those words make you picture? _____

_____

1. What did you picture for the man digging in his vineyard? _____

_____

2. What did you picture for the wall? _____

_____

3. What did you picture for the city getting uncovered? _____

_____

4. What did you picture for the "dead were found in the streets and in their homes"? _____

_____

Critical Thinking

Picture Summary:

Number these in order.

☐ The city lay hidden for hundreds of years after being covered in 30 feet of ash and mud.

☐ In A.D. 79, Mt. Vesuvius, a volcano, erupted in Pompeii.

☐ A man digging in his vineyard uncovered Pompeii, which has since been preserved to show a moment in time.

Main Idea:

Check the box that best describes all your images—the main idea.

☐ With a loud roar, flames and smoke shot out of the volcano, Mt. Vesuvius.

☐ Much of Pompeii has been uncovered to show a moment frozen in time, with people preserved in their homes and on the streets.

☐ Pompeii was destroyed by a volcano and forgotten for hundreds of years, until it was uncovered to show a moment in time.

HOT Questions:

1. Why do you think the cattle and horses were pacing nervously in the fields? _____

_____

2. Why do you think that most people went about their daily lives when the earth first shook that morning? _____

_____

3. What do you think made the earth shake? _____

_____

4. Why do you think some people hid in their homes after the volcano, Mt. Vesuvius, began to erupt? _____

_____

5. What do you think the story meant by "ash and poison gases soon found them"? _____

_____

6. What do you think "frozen in time" means? _____

_____

Make up a story about being in Pompeii the day the volcano erupted.

_____
_____
_____
_____
_____
_____
_____
_____
_____
_____
_____
_____
_____
_____
_____
_____
_____
_____
_____
_____
_____
_____
_____

Did you use all of the Structure Words? Check each one you used.

| ☐ What | ☐ Size | ☐ Color | ☐ Number | ☐ Shape | ☐ Where |
| ☐ Movement | ☐ Mood | ☐ Background | ☐ Perspective | ☐ When | ☐ Sound |

19 The Ice Cream Cone

The ice cream cone was invented on a hot day in 1904. A young man was selling ice cream at the fair. Because it was hot, many people crowded his stand as they waited for their dishes of ice cream. But he soon ran out of clean cups and spoons for his many customers.

Ernest Hamwi, who was selling thin waffle cookies in the next stand, had an idea. He rolled one of his waffles to form a cone. The ice cream seller then filled the waffle with ice cream. Now the crowd could eat ice cream without using a cup. The ice cream cone was a big hit.

Vocabulary:

invented: to make for the first time; to create
waffle: a thin pancake made on a hot iron

---

1 **First Paragraph:** The ice cream cone was invented on a hot day in 1904. A young man was selling ice cream at the fair. Because it was hot, many people crowded his stand as they waited for their dishes of ice cream. But he soon ran out of clean cups and spoons for his many customers.

What did those words make you picture? _____

_____

_____

1. What did you picture for 1904? _____

_____

2. What did you see for the young man selling ice cream? _____

_____

3. What did you picture for the hot weather? _____

_____

4. What did you picture for the man running out of cups and spoons? _____

_____

2 **Second Paragraph:** Ernest Hamwi, who was selling thin waffle cookies in the next stand, had an idea. He rolled one of his waffles to form a cone. The ice cream seller then filled the waffle with ice cream. Now the crowd could eat ice cream without using a cup. The ice cream cone was a big hit.

What did those words make you picture? _____

_____

_____

1. Where did you picture Ernest selling waffle cookies? _____

_____

2. What did you picture for Ernest rolling a waffle to form a cone? _____

_____

3. What did you see the ice cream seller doing with his ice cream? _____

_____

4. What did you picture the crowd doing now? _____

_____

Picture Summary:

Number these in order.

Ernest Hamwi was selling waffle cookies in the next stand, and he rolled one of his waffles to form a cone.

The ice cream cone was invented on a hot day in 1904 at the fair.

People crowded the ice cream stand until the man ran out of spoons and cups.

The ice cream seller filled the cone with ice cream, and the ice cream cone was a big hit.

Write a Word Summary:

_____

_____

_____

_____

_____

_____

_____

Critical Thinking

Main Idea:

Check the box that best describes all your images—the main idea.

☐ Because it was hot, many people crowded the ice cream stand as they waited for their cool treat.

☐ The ice cream seller filled the waffle cone with ice cream.

☐ The ice cream cone was invented when a young man selling ice cream ran out of clean cups and spoons.

HOT Questions:

1. Why do you think so many people wanted ice cream? _____

_____

2. How did a hot day help invent the ice cream cone? _____

_____

3. Why do you think the ice cream seller ran out of cups and spoons? _____

_____

4. Why do you think Ernest wanted to help the ice cream seller? _____

_____

5. Do you think the ice cream seller was happy that Ernest helped him? Why? _____

_____

6. Why do you think the waffle was better for holding the ice cream than the cups? _____

_____

7. Why do you think the ice cream cone became a big hit? _____

_____

Make up a funny story about eating ice cream.

_____

_____

_____

_____

_____

_____

_____

_____

_____

_____

_____

_____

_____

_____

_____

_____

_____

_____

Did you use all of the Structure Words? Check each one you used.
- ☐ What
- ☐ Movement
- ☐ Size
- ☐ Mood
- ☐ Color
- ☐ Background
- ☐ Number
- ☐ Perspective
- ☐ Shape
- ☐ When
- ☐ Where
- ☐ Sound

20 The Mighty Babe Ruth

The New York Yankees were trailing the Chicago Cubs in the third baseball game of the World Series. The Chicago fans yelled and threw lemons as the Yankee hitter, Babe Ruth, picked up his bat and walked to the plate. Charlie Root, the Cub pitcher, reached back and threw the ball. Babe swung and missed. "Strike one!" the umpire yelled.

Babe calmly looked at the pitcher. Root stared at Babe, and then hurled another ball. "Ball one!" cried the umpire, followed by "Ball two!" The Chicago crowd was growing restless as they hoped the mighty Babe Ruth would strike out.

The Chicago pitcher gripped the baseball and hurled it across the plate. Babe took a mighty swing and missed. "Strike two!" the umpire called. Then Babe Ruth stuck out his arm and pointed over the centerfield wall. A moment later, Charlie Root hurled another pitch. With a loud smack, the ball flew right where Babe had just pointed. It was a home run and the Yankees won the baseball game.

Vocabulary:

Babe Ruth: many believe the greate[st] baseball player who ever lived
baseball: a game played with a bat and ball
strike: the pitcher threw the ball ov[er] home plate, but the batter did not hit
ball: the pitcher threw the ball and it did not go over home plate
umpire: the person who says if the pitcher has thrown a ball or a strike

---

1 **First Paragraph:** The New York Yankees were trailing the Chicago Cubs in the third baseball game of the World Series. The Chicago fans yelled and threw lemons as the Yankee hitter, Babe Ruth, picked up his bat and walked to the plate. Charlie Root, the Cub pitcher, reached back and threw the ball. Babe swung and missed. "Strike one!" the umpire yelled.

What did those words make you picture? _____

_____

_____

1. What did you picture for the baseball game? _____

_____

2. What did you picture for Babe Ruth at bat? _____

_____

3. What did you picture the Chicago fans doing? _____

_____

4. What did you picture for Charlie Root, the pitcher, throwing the ball?_____

_____

2 **Second Paragraph:** Babe calmly looked at the pitcher. Root stared at Babe, and then hurled another ball. "Ball one!" cried the umpire, followed by "Ball two!" The Chicago crowd was growing restless as they hoped the mighty Babe Ruth would strike out.

What did those words make you picture? _____

_____

1. What did you picture for Babe at bat now? _____

_____

2. What did you picture Root, the pitcher, doing after he threw two balls? _____

_____

3. What did you picture for the crowd growing restless? _____

_____

4. Were you picturing the crowd up close or from far away? _____

_____

3 **Third Paragraph:** The Chicago pitcher gripped the baseball and hurled it across the plate. Babe took a mighty swing and missed. "Strike two!" the umpire called. Then Babe Ruth stuck out his arm and pointed over the centerfield wall. A moment later, Charlie Root hurled another pitch. With a loud smack, the ball flew right where Babe had just pointed. It was a home run and the Yankees won the baseball game.

What did those words make you picture? _____

_____

1. What did you picture for Babe pointing to centerfield? _____

_____

2. What did you picture for Babe hitting the next pitch? _____

_____

3. What did you picture for the home run? _____

_____

4. What sounds can you hear in this imagery? _____

Critical Thinking

Picture Summary:

Number these in order.

☐ Babe Ruth pointed over the centerfield wall and then smacked the ball right where he pointed.

☐ In the third game of the series, Ruth stepped up and missed, and the umpire called "Strike One!"

☐ The pitcher threw again, and Ruth missed again, as the umpire called "Strike Two!"

Main Idea:

Check the box that best describes all your images—the main idea.

☐ During the World Series, Babe Ruth pointed over the centerfield wall and then hit a home run.

☐ The Chicago pitcher, Charlie Root, gripped the baseball and hurled across the plate.

☐ The Chicago crowd grew restless as they hoped the mighty Babe Ruth would strike out.

HOT Questions:

1. Why do you think the fans of the other team threw lemons at Babe Ruth? _____

_____

2. Why do you think Charlie Root stared at Babe for a moment before throwing the second ball? _____

_____

3. Why do you think the crowd was growing restless with Babe at bat? _____

_____

4. Why do you think Babe was so calm when he was at bat? _____

_____

5. Why do you think Babe pointed to centerfield? _____

_____

6. Do you think Babe knew where he would hit the ball? Why or why not? _____

_____

Write a Word Summary about __The Mighty Babe Ruth.__

_____
_____
_____
_____
_____
_____
_____
_____
_____
_____
_____
_____
_____
_____
_____
_____
_____
_____
_____

Did you use all of the Structure Words? Check each one you used.

☐ What   ☐ Size   ☐ Color   ☐ Number   ☐ Shape   ☐ Where
☐ Movement   ☐ Mood   ☐ Background   ☐ Perspective   ☐ When   ☐ Sound

21 A Hairy Monster

A large hairy monster that looks like a man may live in the woods of North America. For over 400 years, people have told tales of Bigfoot. The stories tell of a tall animal that roams the forests. They say he is covered in long hair like an ape. But he walks like a person.

This large creature is rarely seen. Only a few pictures of him exist. Most of these photos have been taken from a distance and are hard to see. Many people say that Bigfoot is a myth. But some think he is real. Until he is caught, the mystery will remain.

Vocabulary:

North America: a large area of land that includes the U.S., Canada, and Mexico
Bigfoot: a creature that is said to look like a large hairy ape that walks like a man
creature: a scary animal
exist: can be found; are present
myth: an old story that is not true

---

1 **First Paragraph:** A large hairy monster that looks like a man may live in the woods of North America. For over 400 years, people have told tales of Bigfoot. The stories tell of a tall animal that roams the forests. They say he is covered in long hair like an ape. But he walks like a person.

What did those words make you picture? _____

_____

_____

1. What did you picture for the hairy monster? _____

_____

2. Where did you picture the woods that the monster may live in? _____

_____

3. What did you picture for the monster's feet? _____

_____

4. What did you picture for the hair on the monster's body? _____

_____

2 **Second Paragraph:** This large creature is rarely seen. Only a few pictures of him exist. Most of these photos have been taken from a distance and are hard to see. Many people say that Bigfoot is a myth. But some think he is real. Until he is caught, the mystery will remain.

What did those words make you picture? _____

_____

_____

1. What did you see for the photos of Bigfoot? _____

_____

2. How many photos of Bigfoot did you picture? _____

_____

3. What did you picture for the photos that were taken from far away? _____

_____

4. Were you picturing those photos up close or from far away? _____

_____

Picture Summary:

Number these in order.

The stories tell of an animal that looks like an ape but walks like a person.

Rarely has anyone seen this creature and only a few pictures of him exist.

For over 400 years, there have been stories about a large hairy monster in the woods of North America.

Many people say he is a myth, but until he is caught, the mystery will remain.

Write a Word Summary:

_____

_____

_____

_____

_____

_____

Critical Thinking

Main Idea:

Check the box that best describes all your images—the main idea.

☐ The few photos of Bigfoot were taken from a distance and are hard to see.

☐ Bigfoot is a large hairy monster that many believe lives in the woods of North America.

☐ Bigfoot is covered in long hair like an ape but walks like a person.

HOT Questions:

1. Why do you think Bigfoot lives in a wooded area? _____

_____

2. Why do you think Bigfoot has hair all over his body? _____

_____

3. Do you think Bigfoot has big feet? Explain. _____

_____

4. Why do you think Bigfoot is rarely seen? _____

_____

5. Why do you think few photos of Bigfoot exist? _____

_____

6. Why do you think most of the photos are taken from a distance and not from close up? _____

_____

7. Why do you think many people believe Bigfoot is a myth? _____

_____

Make up a scary story about seeing Bigfoot.

_____

_____

_____

_____

_____

_____

_____

_____

_____

_____

_____

_____

_____

_____

_____

_____

_____

Did you use all of the Structure Words? Check each one you used.

☐ What	☐ Size	☐ Color	☐ Number	☐ Shape	☐ Where
☐ Movement	☐ Mood	☐ Background	☐ Perspective	☐ When	☐ Sound

22 Velcro

George de Mestral invented Velcro soon after he found burrs on his pant legs. George had taken a walk in the woods. When he got back, he pulled the dark fuzzy burrs off his pant legs. He was amazed at how well each burr was attached. So George decided to study them more closely.

George took one burr and looked at it under a microscope. The burr had hundreds of small hooks that became attached to whatever it touched. Then George had an idea. He would make a new type of fastener that would work like a burr.

George made a fastener with two sides. One side was covered with small hooks. The other was made of many loops. After lots of hard work, George finished his new product. He called it Velcro.

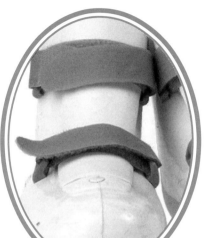

Vocabulary:

Velcro: two pieces of cloth, with tiny hook on one and loops on the other, that are used to fasten things together

burr: a small pod of seeds with hundred of tiny hooks on the outside

microscope: machine that is used to make very small things look larger

fastener: something that is used to hook or close a piece of clothing

---

1 **First Paragraph:** George de Mestral invented Velcro soon after he found burrs on his pant legs. George had taken a walk in the woods. When he got back, he pulled the dark fuzzy burrs off his pant legs. He was amazed at how well each burr was attached. So George decided to study them more closely.

What did those words make you picture? _____

_____

_____

1. What did you picture for George taking a walk? _____

_____

2. What did you picture George getting on his pant legs? _____

_____

3. What did you picture for George trying to pull the burrs off? _____

_____

4. What mood did you picture for George when the burrs were hard to get off? _____

_____

2 **Second Paragraph:** George took one burr and looked at it under a microscope. The burr had hundreds of small hooks that became attached to whatever it touched. Then George had an idea. He would make a new type of fastener that would work like a burr.

What did those words make you picture? _____

_____

1. What did you picture for George using the microscope? _____

_____

2. What did you picture for how the burr looked under the microscope? _____

_____

3. What did you picture for the hundreds of small hooks on the burr? _____

_____

4. What did you picture for George having an idea? _____

_____

3 **Third Paragraph:** George made a fastener with two sides. One side was covered with small hooks. The other was made of many loops. After lots of hard work, George finished his new product. He called it Velcro.

What did those words make you picture? _____

_____

1. What did you picture for a fastener with two sides? _____

_____

2. What did you picture for the small hooks on one side? _____

_____

3. What did you picture for the many loops on the other side? _____

_____

4. What did you picture George doing when he completed the new fastener? _____

_____

Critical Thinking

Picture Summary:

Number these in order.

▢ George made a fastener with two sides, one with small hooks and one with many loops, which he called Velcro.

▢ George invented Velcro after he found burrs on his pants that amazed him by how well they were attached.

▢ George took one burr, looked at it under the microscope, and saw that it had hundreds of small hooks.

Main Idea:

Check the box that best describes all your images—the main idea.

☐ George de Mestral studied some burrs stuck on his pant legs and then invented Velcro.

☐ George de Mestral made a fastener with hooks and loops.

☐ George de Mestral was amazed when he discovered how well each burr was attached to his pant legs.

HOT Questions:

1. Where do you think George got the burrs? _____

_____

2. Why do you think the burrs stuck to George's pants? _____

_____

3. Why do you think George looked at the burrs under a microscope? _____

_____

4. How do you think it helped George to look at the burrs under a microscope? _____

_____

5. Why do you think George wanted to make a fastener with hooks and loops? _____

_____

6. Why was it important to have a hook on one side and a loop on the other? _____

_____

Write a Word Summary about <u>Velcro.</u>

_____

_____

_____

_____

_____

_____

_____

_____

_____

_____

_____

_____

_____

_____

_____

_____

_____

Did you use all of the Structure Words? Check each one you used.

| ☐ What | ☐ Size | ☐ Color | ☐ Number | ☐ Shape | ☐ Where |
| ☐ Movement | ☐ Mood | ☐ Background | ☐ Perspective | ☐ When | ☐ Sound |

23 Grandma Moses

When Grandma Moses was 75 years old, she set down her sewing needle for the last time. Pain in her hands had made it hard for her to sew. Grandma Moses picked up a paintbrush instead.

Grandma Moses painted scenes from her childhood. Her paintings are of life on the farm. They showed everything from the hard work of making candles to the fun of the first snow.

One day an art collector saw some of Grandma Moses' paintings in a store window. He bought them all and took them to New York City. Soon her artwork was being sold all over the world. Grandma Moses had become a famous painter.

Vocabulary:

Grandma Moses: a famous American arti▮
childhood: the time when a person was young
scenes: a view or picture of a place
collector: a person who buys and keeps objects

---

1 **First Paragraph:** When Grandma Moses was 75 years old, she set down her sewing needle for the last time. Pain in her hands had made it hard for her to sew. Grandma Moses picked up a paintbrush instead.

What did those words make you picture? _____

_____

_____

1. What did you picture for Grandma Moses? _____

_____

2. What did you picture for Grandma's age—did you see her old and also see the numbers?_____

_____

3. What did you picture for Grandma's hands as she tried to sew?_____

_____

4. What did you picture for Grandma picking up a paintbrush?_____

_____

2 **Second Paragraph:** Grandma Moses painted scenes from her childhood. Her paintings are of life on the farm. They showed everything from the hard work of making candles to the fun of the first snow.

What did those words make you picture? _____

_____

1. What did you picture for Grandma Moses painting? _____

_____

2. Where did you picture Grandma when she was painting? _____

_____

3. What did you picture for Grandma's paintings? _____

_____

4. What did you picture for Grandma's painting of the first snow? _____

_____

3 **Third Paragraph:** One day an art collector saw some of Grandma Moses' paintings in a store window. He bought them all and took them to New York City. Soon her artwork was being sold all over the world. Grandma Moses had become a famous painter.

What did those words make you picture? _____

_____

1. What did you picture for the art collector? _____

_____

2. What did you picture for Grandma Moses' paintings in a window? _____

_____

3. What did you picture for the collector taking Grandma's paintings to New York City? _____

_____

4. What did you picture for Grandma being famous? _____

Critical Thinking

Picture Summary:

Number these in order.

[■] Grandma Moses set down her needle at 75 and picked up a paintbrush.

[■] An art collector saw some of Grandma Moses' paintings and took them to New York City, making her famous.

[■] Grandma Moses painted scenes from her childhood on the farm.

Main Idea:

Check the box that best describes all your images—the main idea.

☐ Grandma Moses began to paint when she was 75 years old and became a famous artist.

☐ Grandma Moses stopped sewing when she was 75 because it was too hard to hold the small needle.

☐ An art collector bought some of her paintings and took them to New York City.

HOT Questions:

1. Why do you think Grandma Moses had difficulty sewing? _____

_____

2. Why do you think Grandma started painting at such an old age? _____

_____

3. Why do you think painting was easier for Grandma than sewing? _____

_____

4. Why do you think a paintbrush was easier to use than a needle? _____

_____

5. Why do you think Grandma painted scenes from her childhood? _____

_____

6. Why do you think the art collector bought all of the paintings in the store? _____

_____

rite a Word Summary about <u>Grandma Moses.</u>

_____
_____
_____
_____
_____
_____
_____
_____
_____
_____
_____
_____
_____
_____
_____
_____
_____
_____

Did you use all of the Structure Words? Check each one you used.

- ☐ What
- ☐ Movement
- ☐ Size
- ☐ Mood
- ☐ Color
- ☐ Background
- ☐ Number
- ☐ Perspective
- ☐ Shape
- ☐ When
- ☐ Where
- ☐ Sound

24 Hot Dog Champion

A record was broken on July 4 at Nathan's Famous hot dog eating contest. The competitors walked onto the stage. White plates stacked high with hot dogs were placed on a long table. The crowd grew quiet as the hot dog eating contest was about to begin.

A whistle sounded to start eating! The contestants grabbed the hot dogs and ate as fast as they could. As they gobbled and stuffed them in their mouth, the time ticked away.

Then the whistle sounded again! The contest was over. The crowd gasped as the winner was announced. Takeru had eaten 50 hot dogs in 12 minutes. The thin young man stepped forward to get his trophy.

Vocabulary:

champion: the winner
contest: a game where the players try to defeat each other to win a prize
competitors: the people in a contest
gobbled: ate very quickly
announced: said loudly to the public
trophy: a metal cup or statue that is given to the winner of a contest

---

1

First Paragraph: A record was broken on July 4 at Nathan's Famous hot dog eating contest. The competitors walked onto the stage. White plates stacked high with hot dogs were placed on a long table. The crowd grew quiet as the hot dog eating contest was about to begin.

What did those words make you picture? _____

_____

_____

1. What did you picture for the hot dogs? _____

_____

2. What did you picture for the competitors? _____

_____

3. What did you picture for the plates of hot dogs? _____

_____

4. What sounds did you hear in this imagery when the contest was about to begin? _____

_____

2 **Second Paragraph:** A whistle sounded to start eating! The contestants grabbed the hot dogs and ate as fast as they could. As they gobbled and stuffed them in their mouth, the time ticked away.

What did those words make you picture? _____

_____

1. What sound did you hear to signal the start of the contest? _____

_____

2. What did you picture for the contestants eating the hot dogs? _____

_____

3. What did you see for them stuffing the hot dogs in their mouths? _____

_____

4. What did you picture for "the time ticked away"? _____

_____

3 **Third Paragraph:** Then the whistle sounded again! The contest was over. The crowd gasped as the winner was announced. Takeru had eaten 50 hot dogs in 12 minutes. The thin young man stepped forward to get his trophy.

What did those words make you picture? _____

_____

1. What sound did you hear for the signal to stop eating? _____

_____

2. What did you picture for the winner? _____

_____

3. How did you picture Takeru eating 50 hot dogs? _____

_____

4. What did you picture for Takeru getting his trophy? _____

Critical Thinking

Picture Summary:

Number these in order.

███   Takeru ate 50 hot dogs in 12 minutes to win the trophy.

███   A whistle sounded and the contestants grabbed hot dogs and ate as fast as they could.

███   On July 4, at Nathan's Famous hot dog eating contest, the contestants sat in front of a table of hot dogs.

Main Idea:

Check the box that best describes all your images—the main idea.

☐ The contestants grabbed hot dogs and ate as fast as they could as the time ticked away.

☐ On July 4, a thin young man surprised the crowd by eating 50 hot dogs to win the Nathan's Famous hot dog eating contest.

☐ White plates were stacked high with hot dogs before the contest began.

HOT Questions:

1. Why do you think anyone would try to win a hot dog eating contest? _____

_____

2. Why do you think the plates were stacked high with hot dogs? _____

_____

3. Why do you think the contestants ate the hot dogs as fast as they could? _____

_____

4. Why do you think the crowd gasped? _____

_____

5. Why do you think eating 50 hot dogs in 12 minutes was a new record? _____

_____

6. What do you think the winner did after he got his trophy? _____

_____

rite a Word Summary about <u>Hot Dog Champion.</u>

_____

_____

_____

_____

_____

_____

_____

_____

_____

_____

_____

_____

_____

_____

_____

_____

_____

Did you use all of the Structure Words? Check each one you used.

☐ What   ☐ Size   ☐ Color   ☐ Number   ☐ Shape   ☐ Where

☐ Movement   ☐ Mood   ☐ Background   ☐ Perspective   ☐ When   ☐ Sound

Notes

Analysis of Student Performance:

_____

_____

_____

_____

_____

_____

_____

_____

_____

_____

_____

_____

_____

_____

_____

_____

Visualizing and Verbalizing® Graded Workbooks **Color Coding**

The colored checkers along the book's spine represent the grade level of the workbook. For example, the three green checkers indicate that the workbook is written at a third grade reading level. The colored star helps differentiate between books a, b, and c in each workbook set.